The publication of this catalogue was
underwritten by the Wyeth Endowment for American Art.

NB
237
E17
D6
1969

Published by The Corcoran Gallery of Art
Washington, D.C. 20006
Library of Congress Catalog Number 70-87934
Copyright The Corcoran Gallery of Art, 1969
Printed in the United States by Garamond/Pridemark Press,
Baltimore, Md.

THE SCULPTURE OF
THOMAS EAKINS

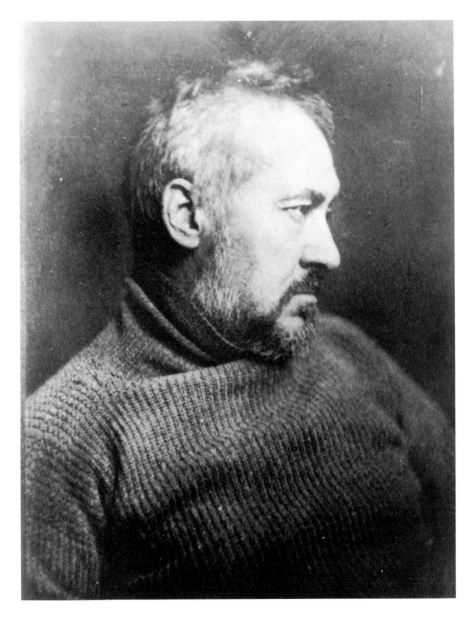

Thomas Eakins   1844-1916

THE SCULPTURE OF
THOMAS EAKINS

Moussa M. Domit

The Corcoran Gallery of Art

May 3—June 10, 1969

TABLE OF CONTENTS

Cover: *Arcadia*
       Catalogue No. 15

Photograph of Thomas Eakins iv
Courtesy Seymour Adelman

Trustees of The Corcoran Gallery of Art vi

Lenders to the Exhibition viii

Foreword 1

Acknowledgments 2

Introduction 3

Notes 13

Catalogue 17

Plates 27

Biography 61

Selected Bibliography 64

Staff of The Corcoran Gallery of Art 66

LENDERS TO THE EXHIBITION

Mr. Seymour Adelman

The Butler Institute of American Art

Joseph H. Hirshhorn Collection

Mr. Maurice Horwitz

The Metropolitan Museum of Art

The State of New Jersey, Department of
Conservation and Economic Development

Pennsylvania Academy of the Fine Arts

Philadelphia Museum of Art

The Art Museum, Princeton University

Mr. and Mrs. James Wyeth

FOREWORD

Although much has been written about Thomas Eakins since his death in 1916 and numerous exhibitions of his paintings have been held, this is the first exhibition and publication to focus on his sculpture.

We are deeply indebted to the Wyeth Endowment for American Art, Mr. Lloyd Goodrich of the Whitney Museum of American Art, Dr. Evan H. Turner of the Philadelphia Museum of Art, Mr. Seymour Adelman, Mr. Joseph Ternbach, Mr. Jack Boucher of the Department of Conservation and Economic Development of the State of New Jersey and Mr. James Wyeth, among others, for their continued assistance and generosity.

The exhibition and the catalogue were prepared by Moussa M. Domit, Assistant Director of the Corcoran Gallery of Art.

James Harithas
Director
The Corcoran Gallery of Art

1

ACKNOWLEDGMENTS

I wish to express my deepest gratitude to all the lenders whose generous cooperation made this exhibition possible, particularly Dr. Evan H. Turner, Director of the Philadelphia Museum of Art, for lending a considerable number of outstanding works by Eakins, including the two plaster studies.

I am indebted to Mr. Lloyd Goodrich for his assistance in locating objects and for making available to me his unpublished notes, which, together with his monumental book and the many articles on Thomas Eakins, have been the basic source of reference for my essay and catalogue on Eakins' sculpture; to Mr. Jack Boucher and Mr. David Pointsett for their enormous help with the loan of the Trenton Battle Monument panels; to Mr. Joseph Ternbach for supervising the dismantling of the Trenton panels and for his skillful cleaning which brought them back to life; to Mr. Seymour Adelman for locating significant information on the statues of the Witherspoon Building.

I would like to thank James Harithas for his invaluable advice in the planning of the exhibition and for editing the text of the introduction in this catalogue; Aldus Chapin for his interest and support of the exhibition; to Mrs. Elise Hamilton, whose help in the organizing of the exhibition and the compiling of the catalog has been immeasurable. I am grateful for the assistance of Mrs. Gretchen Spitz, Mrs. Dorothy Phillips, Miss Martha Morris and Einar Gomo and his staff.

M.M.D

INTRODUCTION

*". . . I have painted many pictures
and done a little sculpture."* [1]

Thomas Eakins

During his lifetime, Thomas Eakins produced only ten complete sculptures, seven of which were commissions, and about seventeen studies. Sculpture for its own sake was of secondary interest to him but, like his interest in anatomy, it appealed to him as an important supplement to painting, i.e., as a means of achieving a greater understanding of mass and volume. His models, which he used as studies for his paintings and reliefs, and his anatomical drawings and casts, reveal a preoccupation with the correct expression of movement in human and animal forms as well as with the accurate physical description of these forms. His brilliant handling of three-dimensional effects and his ability to achieve the utmost clarity of form merit profound consideration not only apart from his paintings but also in relation to particular figures in his paintings which appeared there as a result of his sculptural explorations.

As a painter, Eakins' position in the short history of American art is well established. He is undoubtedly a monumental figure, and his art reflects an individuality unsurpassed in the century in which he lived. But he is also an "isolated figure, belonging to no school, having few ancestors or descendants. It would be difficult to trace any influence in his work." [2] A fully committed "naturalist" [3] and possessing a rare combination of artistic and scientific insights, Eakins felt that the art of his native country, especially the Romantic landscapes of the Hudson River School and Genre painting (both prominent during his youth), was far removed from the realities of life with which he was particularly concerned. In going to Paris to study art, his aim was mainly to learn the technique of painting which he mastered under Jean Léon Gérôme. Neither traditional European art, so richly represented in the Louvre, nor the incipient contemporary movements, for example, Impressionism, seemed to have had much impact on his temperament. Although "his affinities were closer to the independent French artists, such as Courbet, Corot, Degas or Manet; here again the parallels were those of coincidence rather than influence." [4] In this regard, in describing Eakins' style, Lloyd Goodrich has said:

"His art was completely three-dimensional. His forms were in full round, absolutely solid, to the very cores, and convincing in tangibility, hardness and weight . . . he simply felt the physical existence of things with almost primitive integrity . . . The character of forms was stated without softening or idealization, but with uncompromising boldness and saliency." [5]

Eakins' formal training in sculpture was limited. He had learned mechanical and perspective drawing in high school, prior to entering the Pennsylvania Academy of the Fine Arts in Philadelphia, his native city, in 1861. The Academy system at the time emphasized drawing from lifeless classical casts, a method Eakins disliked feeling that, with so many "living" forms in nature, casts as models for art were really unnecessary. He supplemented his training by regularly attending anatomy classes at the Jefferson Medical College. It was not until he went to Paris that he had the brief opportunity to take up sculpture as a separate discipline and as a supplement to his work in drawing and painting. His instructor was Augustin Alexander Dumont (1801-1884), a minor figure, who came from a family of French artists and whose conservative, academic teachings were in keeping with the Beaux Arts' tradition. Eakins also continued to study anatomy which was offered both at the Ecole des Beaux Arts and in a local hospital. "Since I am learning to work clean and bright," he wrote from Paris, "and understand the niceties of color, my anatomy studies and sculpture, especially anatomy, comes to bear on my work and I construct my men more solid and springy and strong." [6]

On his return from Europe, Eakins again took up the subject of anatomy and later taught it at the Pennsylvania Academy, where he also introduced the study of sculpture in his life classes. Both sculpture and anatomy became the foundation of his technique and it was his exhaustive understanding of the two subjects that enabled him to achieve the naturalism so characteristic of his painting.

Eakins approached sculpture with firmness and precision, and the few works he completed during his career reveal not only a mastery of technique but also the vitality and directness so typical of his paintings. All Eakins' completed sculptures are in relief, the underlying principles of which he understood thoroughly; this form presented him with the challenge of relating to both painting and free-standing sculpture. In relief, he was able to explore the possibilities of making recessions and projections and, further, the manner of modeling figures and forms against a background that provides, as in painting and drawing, the illusion of depth. The design required accurate calculation of figures on a parallel plane and in perspective. A further consideration was the play of light and shadow on the overall surface. In a prepared lecture (the manuscript of which, according to Lloyd Goodrich, still exists) on relief as an art form, Eakins said:

". . . Relief holds a place between a painting or drawing on a flat surface and a piece of full sculpture . . . The frieze of the Parthenon by Phidias is the highest reflection of relief. Those things by Phidias, with very little imagination you feel that they stand out full—yet when you get around to the side you see that they are very flat . . . Where the subject of relief becomes complicated, as in the gates of Ghiberti at Florence, and distant landscape, architecture and other accessories are shown, the simple plan above is departed from. The near figures which are of the greatest interest are in full or nearly full relief, and the distant parts have a very flat relief . . . A great disadvantage in such relief as Ghiberti's is that when viewed in the light most favorable for showing the form, the near figures throw shadows on the distant landscape and other parts. This change of scale is a departure from the simplicity of the Greek frieze . . . If you make the least error in a relief it won't look right. There is a limit in relief; if you keep inside of it, it is a powerful instrument to work with. As soon as you do wild things, like the Fighting Gladiator coming toward you, it no longer has that strength." [7]

Eakins' first effort in finished sculpture was a pair of reliefs depicting quiet home scenes, *Spinning* and *Knitting* (nos. 10 and 12). These bear striking similarity to two earlier watercolors, *Spinning* and *Seventy Years Ago* (nos. 9 and 11). The two reliefs were commissioned in 1882 by James P. Scott of Philadelphia as a fireplace decoration in his new house. Although both the subject and the design were assigned by the architect of the house, he (the architect) "easily induced me," Eakins wrote in a letter, "for the work was much to my taste." [8]

The panels were executed in clay and were to be carved in stone but, because of a disagreement over Eakins' fee, Scott refused to accept them and the reliefs remained in Eakins' house until after Mrs. Eakins' death in 1938. Eakins was naturally disturbed and he wrote to Scott and explained that considering the amount of effort the panels required, the fee ($400, according to Lloyd Goodrich), on which there apparently had been an agreement, was perfectly justified. Eakins' letter continues as follows:

"Nor am I an obscure artist. Relief work too has always been considered the most difficult composition and the one requiring the most learning. The mere geometrical construction of the accessories in a perspective which is not projected on a single plane but in a variable third dimension, is a puzzle beyond the sculptors whom I know . . .

"My interest in my work does not terminate with the receipt of my bill. Thus I have heard with dismay that a stonecutter had offered to finish those panels each in a week's time. I have been twenty years studying the naked figure, modeling, painting, drawing, dissecting, teaching. How can any stonecutter unacquainted with the nude, follow my lines, especially, covered as they are, not obscured, by the light draperies? How could the life be retained?" [9]

Eakins worked hard on the panels. The young woman who sat for *Spinning* had to take spinning lessons in order to give him the proper pose. He wrote that, after he had "worked some weeks, the girl in learning to spin well became so much more graceful than when she had learned to spin only passably, that I tore up all my work and recommenced." [10] According to Mrs. Eakins, he did the head of the old woman in *Knitting* three times before he was satisfied with it.[11]

Because he was preoccupied with real life, Eakins paid little attention to romantic or idyllic subjects. The few Arcadian paintings and reliefs (nos. 13, 15, 16, 17) appear to illustrate his inability to cope with imaginary themes. Neither the landscape nor the figures in the Metropolitan's canvas, *Arcadia*, (no. 13) seem to be far removed from Eakins' immediate environment. Even in its unfinished state, the painting has a stark naturalism that is reminiscent of Manet's *Luncheon on the Grass*. In particular, a comparison can be drawn between the three nudes in the Eakins and the nude figure in the foreground of the Manet composition. The relief *Arcadia* in the exhibition is again more of an elaborate study of the human form itself. All his life, Eakins admired the nude, both female and male. And although he had the opportunity at the Beaux Arts to draw and paint from nude models (a method he introduced to the Pennsylvania Academy's life classes together with actual dissections of animals and cadavers [12]), he was not able, due to the prudish Victorian attitude of his time, to reproduce the nude as openly as he often wished.

For the *William Rush Carving His Allegorical Figure of the Schuylkill River* (no. 1), his first painting with a complete nude, he prepared six small wax models (nos. 2a-e), which, together with the four horses (nos. 4a-d), also in wax, for *The Fairman Rogers Four-in-Hand*, constituted Eakins' entire existing oeuvre of three-dimensional, free-standing sculptures. It is known that he also made wax models, none of which have survived, for *The Swimming Hole*.[13] Only five of the original *Rush* figures now exist, including the fine portrait of Rush himself (no. 2a) and, although all these are essentially studies, their freedom of expression, coupled with Eakins' precision and competent handling of mass and modeling, makes them complete works of art.

Eakins' second commission was much more ambitious: two life-size statues of horses for the equestrian figures of Abraham Lincoln and Ulysses S. Grant for the Memorial Arch in Prospect Park, Brooklyn. The commission was secured for him by the sculptor, William R. O'Donovan, a friend and an admirer. O'Donovan was to do the figures of Lincoln and Grant. Eakins loved horses and had made models and anatomical studies of them (nos. 5, 6, 8). In addition, he also had dissected them in anatomy classes and had made photographic studies of them in motion. With his considerable knowledge of anatomy, Eakins was unquestionably the best candidate for the modeling of the two horses.

Eakins chose as model for Lincoln's horse his own gentle Billy, a farm horse, symbolically appropriate for the "Man of the People." For Grant he chose Clinker, a thoroughbred, which belonged to A. J. Cassatt of Chesterbrook Farm, Berwyn, Pennsylvania. After preparing several studies in clay of the two horses, Eakins made a full-sized model of each in profile. The models were built in sections from life and joined together against a flat background in high relief. Eakins' interpretation of the horses is typically realistic and compassionate. The gentility and poise of Billy and the movement and vitality of Clinker are profound expressions of the beauty of animal forms. Such expressions were rarely achieved in 19th century American sculpture.

In the early 1890's, Eakins was asked, again through the effort of O'Donovan, to do two large (55″ x 94″ each) bronze reliefs representing two major Revolutionary events, *The Battle of Trenton* and *The American Army Crossing the Delaware* [14], for the Battle Monument in Trenton, New Jersey. O'Donovan created the gigantic statue of George Washington which crowns the 135 foot tower and the two rugged figures of Private John Russell and Private Blair McClenachan which flank the entrance way to the monument. Eakins' panels were completed in 1893 and placed in niches on the base of the monument (about 25 feet above the ground) with *The American Army Crossing the Delaware* on the west wall and *The Battle of Trenton* over the entrance. In the program dedication of the monument, which took place on October 19, 1893, a photograph with separate portraits of Eakins and of O'Donovan was reproduced with a note to the effect that Eakins was responsible for the design of the panels. Also included in the presentation is a detailed description of the subjects. The note reads as follows:

> "These two bronze bas-reliefs of the crossing of the river and the battery in action were designed by Thomas Eakins of Philadelphia. Mr. Eakins received his art education in Paris, studying under the celebrated Jean Léon Gérôme. He is now professor of painting and director of the Art Students' League in Philadelphia and lecturer on anatomy at

the Academy of Design in New York City. He received a medal of honor from the World's Columbian Exposition."

The plaster models for these panels have apparently been destroyed, but photographs of them were taken by Eakins himself and the negatives still exist in a private collection.

Eakins spared no effort to achieve almost photographic [15] accuracy in these scenes. One recognizes the buildings on King Street as they stood at the time of the battle. They most probably were still standing in more or less original condition in 1893. The program of the dedication mentions the Stacy Potts' house, Colonel Rall's headquarters, the Green Tree Tavern and several portraits of distinguishd men—James Monroe, Colonel Knox, Captain William Washington.[16]

Of all Eakins' students who became life-long friends, the sculptor Samuel Murray was perhaps the closest to the artist. The two were inseparable and Murray consistently sought the "Master's" advice. The two penetrating portraits of Eakins by Murray in the exhibition (nos. 23 and 24) are a profound tribute to a teacher and friend. From 1895 to 1896, Murray and Eakins collaborated on a sculptural project for the Witherspoon Building in Philadelphia.[17] The commission was Murray's and it was for ten nine-foot statues of prophets to be placed in niches on the exterior of the eighth floor of the building. Eakins supposedly worked with Murray on all of the figures.[18] The statues were made of terra cotta, an impractical medium for outdoor sculpture, so that over the years they suffered much damage from erosion and chipping. The "Prophets" were removed from the Witherspoon Building some years ago when the exterior of the building was remodeled and eight of the statues were given to the Philadelphia Memorial Cemetery in Frazier, Pennsylvania, where six have been completely destroyed by vandals and the remaining two are now covered with whitewash.

Although several of Eakins' small relief models and studies have been destroyed and some are missing (see page 26), this first presentation of his sculpture brings together a fairly comprehensive survey of his existing work in the medium, as well as related paintings and sketches.

The sculpture of Thomas Eakins is based on sound technical principles and created with a penetrating vision. His forms are beautifully constructed with a great sense of volume, solidity and weight. Like his paintings, his completed reliefs and even his model studies are an expression of reality as he saw and felt it. Again, for Eakins, the medium was not an end in itself, but a discipline in understanding the elements of structure and mass which in turn he recreated in his paintings in pure and vivid forms.

Moussa M. Domit
Assistant Director
The Corcoran Gallery of Art

NOTES

1. From a biographical sketch written by Eakins in 1893 in answer to a request for information about himself from a publisher of a biographical dictionary. The entire statement as quoted by Lloyd Goodrich in his *Thomas Eakins, His Life and Work,* reads as follows: "I was born July 25, 1844. My father's father was from the north of Ireland of the Scotch Irish. On my mother's side my blood is English and Hollandish. I was a pupil of Gérôme (also of Bonnat and of Dumont, sculptor). I have taught in life classes, and lectured on anatomy continuously since 1873. I have painted many pictures and done a little sculpture. For the public I believe my life is all in my work. Yours truly, Thomas Eakins."

2. Lloyd Goodrich. *Thomas Eakins, His Life and Work* (New York: Whitney Museum of American Art, 1933), p. 154

3. "His art can be called naturalistic only in relative terms, only in comparison with the swooning romanticism that distorted the natural appearance of objects in the service of extremely personal vision. Eakins was a realist in the most profound sense—a sane, practical and reflective man who found that the mere fact of existence of the world was beautiful in itself, and who asked no greater satisfaction than to observe it and to explore its structure." John Canaday. "Thomas Eakins," *Horizon* Vol. VI, Number 4 (Autumn, 1964) : p. 92

4. Goodrich, op. cit., p. 154

5. Ibid., p. 148

6. Ibid., p. 25

7. Ibid., pp. 63-64

8. Ibid., p. 64

9. Ibid., pp. 64-65

10. Ibid., p. 64

11. Lloyd Goodrich. Notes Unpublished

12. Margaret McHenry. *Thomas Eakins Who Painted* (Privately Printed for the Author: 1946), p. 30

13. Sylvan Schendler. *Eakins* (Boston, Toronto: Little, Brown and Company, 1967), p. 86

14. Reproduced in *The Arts* (December, 1923), p. 304

15. It is possible that Eakins worked from photographs taken on the actual locations of the events.

16. ". . . The relief on the west side represents 'The Continental Army Crossing the Delaware.' This design departs widely from the crossing as depicted by Leutze in his celebrated picture, so faulty in its delineation of the direction of the passage of the boats, in the kind of boats used, in the representation of the ice, and of the flag carried by the American Army. In this design the Durham boats which General Washington directed to be collected from the upper waters of the Delaware during his march through the Jerseys appear as they were used in transporting the horses and artillery. In the immediate foreground is Captain William Washington and the Lieutenant of his Company, James Monroe, afterward President of the United States. Both of these officers were wounded in the battle at Trenton. With them, evidently alarmed at some noise on the New Jersey shore, is Colonel Edward Hand, and the Pennsylvania regiment of sharpshooters, commanded by that gallant officer. The current is swift and the passage dangerous on account of the early winter ice which drifted roughly against the boats, requiring great skill in handling them. The little boat in the foreground contains General Washington and Colonel Knox the artillerist and a Jersey farmer is rowing them over the river. This tablet is presented to the Association by the Commonwealth of Pennsylvania.

"On the south side is the relief showing 'The Opening of the Fight.' The battery of Captain Hamilton is represented as about to fire the first shot at the enemy on King Street. The mounted figure of this brave soldier, who afterward became the gifted statesman, is conspicuous in the foreground. This officer was then only nineteen years of age and his company of New York artillerists were all young men, but it was said to have been a model of discipline. How delighted they must have been on that winter morning to know that the first three balls from their gun killed and wounded eight men, killed three horses and dismounted a gun . . . The houses then standing on the west side of King Street are carefully reproduced on the relief, showing the residence of Isaac Brearley, nearest by, and the Green Tree Tavern and the Stacy Potts' house, Colonel Rall's Headquarters, in the distance. This tablet is presented by the State of New York."

17. McHenry. op. cit., pp. 127-128

18. Two of the ten prophets were bought by Arthur Garrett of Skagway, Alaska, where they will be eventually installed, according to Mr. Garrett, in the courtyard of a newly-constructed church. The information on the "Prophets" was made possible through the effort of Mr. Seymour Adelman, a friend of Mrs. Eakins and Samuel Murray, and a devoted admirer of Eakins. He has recently purchased the house on Mount Vernon Street where Eakins lived and worked all his life, and Mr. Adelman is in the process of having the house restored and presented to the City of Philadelphia as a monument to the artist.

19. ". . . The remarkably fine hand of Margaret Eakins, cast in bronze by Thomas Eakins, was cherished by the Crowell family. It was cherished all the more when the family discovered that in the third generation Frances the Second, Arthur's daughter, had a hand almost identical." McHenry, op. cit., p. 95

20. Two full-sized models for the bronze casts have been destroyed. Also, the whereabouts of the plaster relief from which the bronze cast in the exhibition was made and the smaller plaster studies for both *Clinker* and *Billy* are unknown. Eakins' plaster models and complete sculpture were in Mrs. Eakins' possession until her death in 1938, when they were dispersed as part of the estate and sold. She had had nearly all of them cast in bronze. The few uncast pieces included the small model for *Billy* which was found missing. In an unpublished letter of June 5, 1931, to Lloyd Goodrich, Mrs. Eakins writes: "About the model of the horse, Billy, Mr. Murray and I are both distressed. It was the same size as the big relief which I have of Clinker. I have searched everywhere about the house, if it

was brought here it would have been in my care, as the other casts were. Murray was astonished when I told him I did not have it, he could hardly believe me. He said it was even finer than the Clinker, it seemed to have even more loving work, being my husband's own horse. I feel wretched about it."

CATALOGUE

All works in the exhibition are illustrated.

Numbers of the illustrations correspond to catalogue numbers.

Unless otherwise noted, all casts in bronze are from the original plaster.

Dimensions are given in inches, height precedes width. With sculpture, height includes base.

Listings are not always in chronological order.

Abbreviations: u.l.=upper left; u.r.=upper right; l.l.=lower left; l.r.= lower right; u.c.=upper center; l.c.=lower center; L.G.=Lloyd Goodrich.

CATALOGUE

1. WILLIAM RUSH CARVING HIS ALLEGORICAL FIGURE
   OF THE SCHUYLKILL RIVER   1877
   oil on canvas
   20⅛ x 26½
   signed l.r.: "EAKINS 77"; on back: "T.E."
   Lent by the Philadelphia Museum of Art

2. STUDIES FOR "WILLIAM RUSH"   ca. 1877

   a. HEAD OF RUSH
      bronze
      7¼ high
      unsigned
      Lent by Seymour Adelman

   b. HEAD OF THE MODEL
      plaster (cast from wax)
      7¼ high
      unsigned
      Lent by the Philadelphia Museum of Art

   c. GEORGE WASHINGTON
      bronze
      8⅜ high
      unsigned
      Lent by Seymour Adelman

   d. NYMPH WITH BITTERN
      bronze
      9¼ high
      unsigned
      Lent by Seymour Adelman

   e. THE SCHUYLKILL FREED
      plaster (cast from wax)
      4¾ high
      unsigned
      Lent by the Philadelphia Museum of Art

3. THE FAIRMAN ROGERS FOUR-IN-HAND   1879
oil on canvas
24 x 36
signed l.l.: "EAKINS 79"

This painting, originally called *A May Morning in the Park,* was presented to the Philadelphia Museum in 1930 by a relative of Fairman Rogers, who requested that the painting be given its present title. Fairman Rogers was a prominent Philadelphian and, at the time, a director of The Pennsylvania Academy of the Fine Arts and Chairman of the Committee on Instruction. He was also a friend and admirer of Eakins.
Lent by the Philadelphia Museum of Art

4. FOUR STUDIES OF HORSES FOR THE PAINTING "THE FAIRMAN ROGERS FOUR-IN-HAND"
bronze

   a. RIGHT LEADER

   b. LEFT LEADER

   c. RIGHT WHEELER

   d. LEFT WHEELER

10¼ high and 12¼ long each
unsigned
Lent by the Philadelphia Museum of Art

5. SKELETON   1878
bronze
11 x 14
signed l.c.: "EAKINS 78"

This is an anatomical study for *The Mare Josephine* (no. 8)
Lent by The Butler Institute of American Art

6. ECORCHE   1882
bronze
22½ x 29
signed l.c.: "EAKINS 1882"

This is an anatomical study for *The Mare Josephine* (no. 8)
Lent by the Philadelphia Museum of Art

7. STUDY OF A HORSE IN "THE FAIRMAN ROGERS FOUR-IN-HAND"   ca. 1879
oil on panel
14⅝ x 10⅜
signed on label, l.r.: *"Sketch / 'Boatman' / T. Eakins"*
Originally on the reverse of *Sketch for "The Boatman"*
Lent by the Philadelphia Museum of Art

8. THE MARE JOSEPHINE   1878
bronze
22 x 28
signed l.c.: "EAKINS 78"

Josephine was one of the horses in the painting *The Fairman Rogers Four-in-Hand*
(no. 3)
Lent by the Philadelphia Museum of Art

9. SPINNING   1881
watercolor on paper
14 x 10⅞
signed u.r.: "EAKINS 81."

This watercolor is related in pose and composition to the bronze relief *Spinning*. Originally called *Homespun* (L.G.). The model is the artist's sister, Margaret (L.G.).
Lent by The Metropolitan Museum of Art, Fletcher Fund, 1925

10. SPINNING   1882-1883
bronze
18 x 14½, oval
unsigned
A companion piece to *Knitting* (no. 12); the plaster signed: "SPINNING. THOMAS EAKINS, 1881"   (L.G.)
Lent by the Pennsylvania Academy of the Fine Arts

11. SEVENTY YEARS AGO   1877
    watercolor on paper
    12 x 9
    signed u.r.: "EAKINS 77."
    The model also appears in the plaster relief *Knitting* (no. 12) and as the chaperone in the painting *William Rush Carving His Allegorical Figure of the Schuylkill River* (no. 1). It is related in pose and composition to *Knitting* (no. 12).
    Lent by The Art Museum, Princeton University

12. KNITTING   1881
    plaster (cast from original)
    18½ x 14⅞, oval
    unsigned

    A companion piece to *Spinning* (no. 10); the original plaster signed: "KNITTING. THOMAS EAKINS, 1881" (L. G.).

    The model is "Aunt Sallie," Mrs. King (L.G.), a relative of the Crowell family. William Crowell, high school friend of Eakins, married Eakins' sister, Frances. Eakins was engaged to Katherine Crowell, who died before they were married.
    Collection The Corcoran Gallery of Art

13. ARCADIA   1883
    oil on canvas
    38¾ x 45½
    signed on back: "T. Eakins Pinxit"
    unfinished
    Lent by The Metropolitan Museum of Art, Bequest of Adelaide Milton de Groot (1876-1967), 1967

14. A LADY WITH A SETTER DOG   1885
    oil on canvas
    30 x 23
    unsigned

    The relief *Arcadia* appears in the upper right side of the painting.

    The sitter is Mrs. Eakins (Susan Macdowell Eakins) with the red setter, Harry, the family dog.
    Lent by The Metropolitan Museum of Art, Fletcher Fund, 1923

15. ARCADIA   1883
    bronze
    12½ x 25
    signed u.l.: "EAKINS"; u.c.: "1888" (erroneously dated)

    Original plaster signed: "EAKINS 1883" (L.G.)

    Lent by James Wyeth

16. YOUTH PLAYING THE PIPES   ca. 1883
    oil on panel (Sketch)
    14½ x 10¼
    unsigned

    Lent by Maurice Horwitz

17. YOUTH PLAYING THE PIPES   1883
    bronze
    19¾ x 11
    signed l.r.: "T.E. 1888" (erroneously dated); "THOMAS EAKINS"

    Original plaster signed: "T.E. 1883" (L.G.)

    Lent by the Joseph H. Hirshhorn Collection

18. CLINKER   1892
    bronze
    25½ x 25½
    signed l.c.: "EAKINS 1892"

    Inscribed u.l.: *"Clinker / charger belonging to / A. J. Cassatt,
    Esq. / Chesterbrook Farm / Berwyn, Penna"*

    This is a model for General Grant's horse on the Memorial Arch,
    Prospect Park, Brooklyn.

    Lent by the Philadelphia Museum of Art

19. THE AMERICAN ARMY CROSSING THE DELAWARE
1893

bronze
55 x 94

Inscribed l.l.: *"Presented by the Commonwealth of Pennsylvania"*
The coat of arms of the State of Pennsylvania appears in l.l. corner. This and the following panel were dismantled from the Trenton Battle Monument in Trenton, New Jersey, especially for this exhibition.

Lent by the State of New Jersey, Department of Conservation and Economic Development

20. THE BATTLE OF TRENTON   1893
bronze
55 x 94

Inscribed l.l.: *"Presented by the State of New York"*; u.l., on signpost: *"PERSEVERANTIA"*

The coat of arms of the State of New York appears in l.l. corner.

Lent by the State of New Jersey, Department of Conservation and Economic Development

21. CASTS OF ANATOMICAL DISSECTIONS   early 1880's
bronze

a. DORSAL LEFT SHOULDER
   18¼ long

b. FOOT   1880
   12½ long

c. HAND   1880
   10½ long

d. LEFT SHOULDER, ARM AND HAND
   30 long

e. LEFT SIDE OF NECK
   9 long

f.   MALE VENTRAL TORSO
    28 long

g.   RIGHT SKULL PROFILE
    12 long

h.   RIGHT THIGH, LEG AND FOOT
    39½ long

i.   THROAT AND NECK
    8½ long
unsigned
These were cast from the original plaster after Eakins' death.
Lent by the Philadelphia Museum of Art

22.   CAST OF HAND AND FOREARM   date unknown
    bronze
    12 long
    unsigned
    This is probably the hand of Eakins' sister, Margaret (see note no. 19)
    Lent by the Joseph H. Hirshhorn Collection

23.   THOMAS EAKINS SEATED CROSS-LEGGED WITH HIS PALETTE   1907
    by Samuel Murray
    bronze
    9 high
    signed on base: "MURRAY 1907"
    Lent by The Metropolitan Museum of Art, Rogers Fund, 1923

24.   THOMAS EAKINS   1894
    by Samuel Murray
    bronze
    23 high
    Inscribed on base: "TO MY / DEAR MASTER / SAMUEL MURRAY / 1894
    Lent by the Pennsylvania Academy of the Fine Arts

The following is a list of sculptures known to have been in existence but at present their whereabouts are unknown:

AN ARCADIAN   1883
bronze
8¼ x 5
signed: "THOMAS EAKINS"
This was recorded in *Thomas Eakins, His Life and Work* by Lloyd Goodrich (catalogue no. 507). The same work was exhibited at M. Knoedler and Company in June, 1944, in an exhibition commemorating the centennial of Eakins' birth, and is recorded in the catalogue of the exhibition (no. 88).

BILLY   ca. 1892
plaster
25 x 26
This was recorded in *Thomas Eakins, His Life and Work* by Lloyd Goodrich (catalogue no. 512). Also, see unpublished letter from Mrs. Eakins to Lloyd Goodrich (note no. 20), and *Thomas Eakins Who Painted* by Margaret McHenry, p. 97.

CLINKER   (smaller version) 1892
bronze
6¼ x 6¼
signed u.r.: "THOMAS EAKINS 1892"
This was recorded in *Thomas Eakins, His Life and Work* by Lloyd Goodrich (catalogue no. 510).

MRS. MARY HALLOCK GREENEWALT   1905
plaster
16½ x 12½
inscribed: "MARY HALLOCK GREENEWALT MCMV"
This was recorded in *Thomas Eakins, His Life and Work* by Lloyd Goodrich (catalogue no. 515). Lloyd Goodrich also made a sketch of this plaster portrait which is still in his possession.

The following was not available for this exhibition:

SKETCH FOR MEMORIAL ARCH   ca. 1893
wax
6¾ x 11¾
Collection the Joseph H. Hirshhorn Collection

PLATES

1. *William Rush Carving His Allegorical*
   Figure of the Schuylkill River 1877
   Oil on canvas
   Lent by the Philadelphia Museum of Art

2. *Studies for "William Rush"*   ca. 1877
   Plaster
   Courtesy the Philadelphia Museum of Art

2 a. *Head of Rush*   ca. 1877
Bronze
Lent by Seymour Adelman

2 b. *Head of the Model*   ca. 1877
    Plaster
    Lent by the Philadelphia Museum of Art

2 c. *George Washington* ca. 1877
Bronze
Lent by Seymour Adelman

2 d. *Nymph With Bittern* ca. 1877
Bronze
Lent by Seymour Adelman

2 e. *The Schuylkill Freed*   ca. 1877
Plaster
Lent by the Philadelphia Museum of Art

3. *The Fairman Rogers Four-in-Hand* 1879
Oil on canvas
Lent by the Philadelphia Museum of Art

4. *Four Studies of Horses for the painting*
   "The Fairman Rogers Four-in-Hand"   1879
   Bronze
   Lent by the Philadelphia Museum of Art

4 a. *Right Leader*　1879
Bronze
Lent by the Philadelphia
Museum of Art

4 b. *Left Leader*　1879
Bronze
Lent by the Philadelphia
Museum of Art

4 c. *Right Wheeler* 1879
Bronze
Lent by the Philadelphia
Museum of Art

4 d. *Left Wheeler* 1879
Bronze
Lent by the Philadelphia
Museum of Art

5. *Skeleton* 1878
   Bronze
   Lent by the Butler Institute of American Art

6. *Ecorché* 1882
Bronze
Lent by the Philadelphia Museum of Art

7. *Study of a Horse in "The Fairman Rogers
   Four-in-Hand"* ca. 1879
   Oil on panel
   Lent by the Philadelphia Museum of Art

8. *The Mare Josephine*　1878
   Bronze
   Lent by the Philadelphia Museum of Art

9. *Spinning*   1881
   Watercolor on paper
   Lent by the Metropolitan Museum of Art, Fletcher Fund, 1925

10. *Spinning*   1882-1883
Bronze
Lent by the Pennsylvania Academy of the Fine Arts

11. *Seventy Years Ago* 1877
    Watercolor on paper
    Lent by The Art Museum, Princeton University

12. *Knitting* 1881
    Plaster (cast from original)
    Collection The Corcoran Gallery of Art

13. *Arcadia* 1883
    Oil on canvas
    Lent by The Metropolitan
    Museum of Art, Bequest of
    Adelaide Milton de Groot
    (1876-1967), 1967

14. *A Lady With A Setter Dog*
    1885
    Oil on canvas
    Lent by The Metropolitan
    Museum of Art, Fletcher Fund,
    1923

15. *Arcadia*   1883
Bronze
Lent by James Wyeth

16. *Youth Playing the Pipes*   ca. 1883
    Oil on panel
    Lent by Maurice Horwitz

17. *Youth Playing the Pipes*   1883
Bronze
Lent by the Joseph H. Hirshhorn Collection

Clinker (detail from full-size plaster model)
Photograph taken by Thomas Eakins
Courtesy Seymour Adelman

18. *Clinker*   1892
    Bronze
    Lent by the Philadelphia Museum of Art

Detail of no. 19 (before cleaning)

19. *The American Army Crossing the Delaware*   1893
Bronze
Lent by the State of New Jersey, Department of Conservation and
Economic Development

20. *The Battle of Trenton*   1893
Bronze
Lent by the State of New Jersey, Department of Conservation and
Economic Development

Plaster models of nos. 19 and 20, photographs by Thomas Eakins, courtesy Seymour Adelman

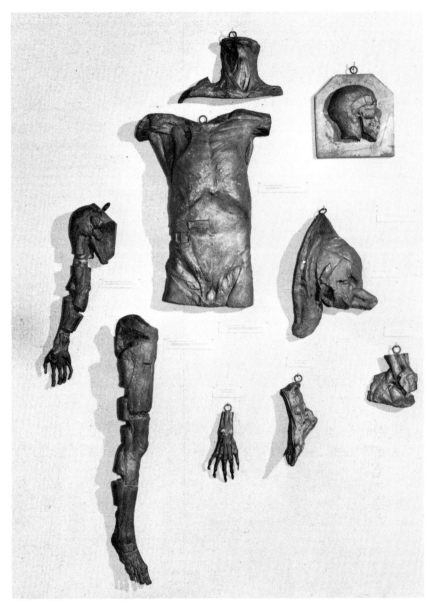

21. *Casts of Anatomical Dissections*   early 1880's
Bronze
Lent by the Philadelphia Museum of Art

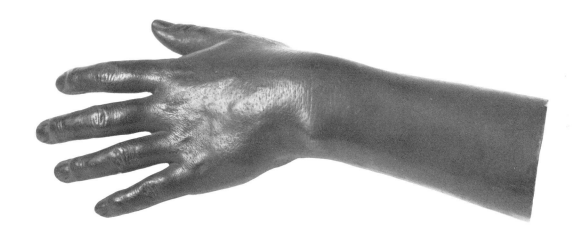

22. *Cast of Hand and Forearm*　date unknown
Bronze
Lent by the Joseph H. Hirshhorn Collection

23. *Thomas Eakins Seated Cross-Legged With His Palette*   1907
by Samuel Murray
Bronze
Lent by The Metropolitan Museum of Art, Rogers Fund, 1923

24. *Thomas Eakins* 1894
    by Samuel Murray
    Bronze
    Lent by the Pennsylvania Academy of the Fine Arts

From left to right: Murray, Eakins and O'Donovan appear in this photograph taken at the time of Eakins' and Murray's collaboration on the "Prophets" for the Witherspoon Building. Photograph reproduced in the October 1895 issue of *McClure's Magazine*
Courtesy The Library of Congress

Thomas Eakins sculpting "Billy" at his sister Frances Eakins Crowell's farm near Avondale, Pennsylvania
Courtesy Seymour Adelman

BIOGRAPHY

SELECTED BIBLIOGRAPHY

BIOGRAPHY

1844   Born 25 July in Philadelphia, Pennsylvania, to Benjamin and Caroline Cowperthwait Eakins, the only son of four children. Father was a writing master.

1846   Moves to 1729 Mount Vernon Street with family.

1857   Enters Central High School in Philadelphia.

1861-66 Studies drawing at The Pennsylvania Academy of the Fine Arts and anatomy at Jefferson Medical College.

1866-69 In Paris, studies painting under Gérôme and Bonnat and sculpture under Dumont at the Ecole des Beaux Arts.

1869   Trip to Spain, December, 1869, to June, 1870.

1870   Returns to Philadelphia.

1876   Volunteers to take over the life classes at The Pennsylvania Academy of the Fine Arts.

1877   Paints *William Rush Carving His Allegorical Figure of the Schuylkill River*.

1879   Becomes teacher at the Pennsylvania Academy of the Fine Arts. Paints *The Fairman Rogers Four-in-Hand*.

1882   Commissioned by James P. Scott to do two oval relief sculptures: *Spinning* and *Knitting*. Becomes Director of the Pennsylvania Academy of the Fine Arts.

1883   Paints *Arcadia* and occupies himself with painting and sculpting idyllic subjects. *Spinning* and *Knitting* are rejected.

1884   Marries Susan Hannah Macdowell.

1884-85 Begins series of experiments with photographs of horses and nude athletes in motion.

1886   Resigns as Director from the Pennsylvania Academy of the Fine Arts. Establishment of the Art Students' League of Philadelphia. Beginning of friendship with Samuel Murray.

1888-98 Lectures on anatomy at the National Academy of Design and at Cooper Union in New York.

1891   Works with William R. O'Donovan on the equestrian statues of Lincoln and Grant for the Memorial Arch in Prospect Park, Brooklyn.

1893   Receives a commission for the two bronze relief panels for the Trenton Battle Monument.

1894   Collaborates with Samuel Murray on the "Prophets" for the Witherspoon Building, Philadelphia.

1896   First and only one-man exhibition at the Earle Galleries in Philadelphia.

1902   Elected "Associate" of the National Academy of Design. Four months later, elected "Academician."

1916   Eakins dies 25 June.

SELECTED BIBLIOGRAPHY

Books

Goodrich, Lloyd. *Thomas Eakins, His Life and Work.* New York, the Whitney Museum of American Art, 1933

McHenry, Margaret. *Thomas Eakins Who Painted.* 1946 (privately published for the author)

McKinney, Roland. *Thomas Eakins.* New York: Crown Publishers, 1942

Porter, Fairfield. *Thomas Eakins.* New York: Braziller, 1959

Schendler, Sylvan. *Eakins.* Boston, Toronto: Little, Brown and Company, 1967

Bulletins and Catalogues

M. Knoedler and Company, New York. *A Loan Exhibition of the Works of Thomas Eakins, Commemorating the Centennial of His Birth, 1844-1944.* New York, 1944

The Metropolitan Museum of Art, New York. *Catalogue of the Loan Exhibition of the Works of Thomas Eakins.* Introduction by Bryson Burroughs. New York, 1917

National Gallery of Art, Washington, D.C.; The Art Institute of Chicago; Philadelphia Museum of Art. *Thomas Eakins. A Retrospective Exhibition.* Introduction by Lloyd Goodrich. 1961

Pennsylvania Academy of the Fine Arts, Philadelphia. *Memorial Exhibition of the Works of the Late Thomas Eakins.* Introduction by Gilbert Sunderland. 1917

Philadelphia Museum of Art, *Bulletin.* "A May Morning in the Park" by Gordon Hendricks. 1965 (Spring), pp. 46-64

Periodicals

Canaday, John. "Thomas Eakins." *Horizon* VI, no. 4, 1964 (Autumn)

Hendricks, Gordon. "Eakins' 'William Rush Carving His Allegorical Figure of the Schuylkill River'." *The Art Quarterly*, XXXI, no. 4, 1968 (winter), pp. 383-404

Katz, Leslie. "Thomas Eakins Now." *Arts*, XXX, no. 12, 1956 (Sept.), pp. 18-23

Moffett, Cleveland. "Grant and Lincoln in Bronze." *McClure's Magazine*, 1895 (Oct.), pp. 419-432

Watkins, Franklin. "Eakins. Philadelphia's Centenary of Its Leading XIX Century Artist: A Painter's Appreciation of the Tradition He Once Combatted." *Art News*, XVIII, no. 1, 1944 (April 15), pp. 11-13

66